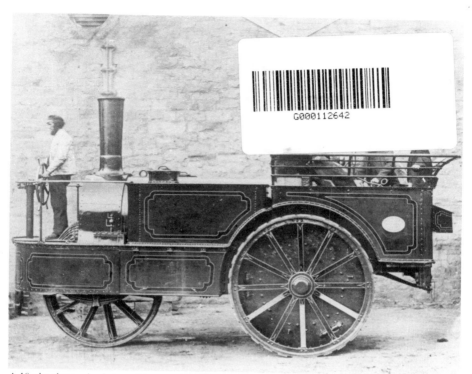

A 10 nhp three-wheeled road locomotive of about 1870 by T. M. Tennant and Company, of Leith in Scotland. It represents a Scottish engineer's idea of what a road steam haulage machine should look like, as opposed to the English preference for a general purpose agricultural engine. The cylinders, probably two in number, are located, railway locomotive fashion, under the smokebox. The purpose of the unusual blanking-off plate behind the hind wheel is unknown, nor are there any indications of a flywheel. The regulator valve, located inside the dome, was controlled from the handle which the bearded driver holds in his left hand. Robert William Thompson (1822-73), Scottish inventor of both pneumatic and solid rubber tyres as well as the three-wheeled, upright-boilered, rubber-tyred Thompson-type road steamers, had his first engine made for him in 1867 by Tennants, whose engineering business lasted only from 1862 until 1871.

TRACTION ENGINES

Harold Bonnett

Shire Publications Ltd

CONTENTS

Set in 9 point Times roman and printed in Great Britain by C. I. Thomas & Sons (Haverfordwest) Ltd, Press Buildings, Merlins Bridge, Haverfordwest, Dyfed.
British Library Cataloguing in Publication data available.

COVER: *This magnificently restored showman's engine is a Fowler B6 class 'Super Lion', 10 nhp, 22½ tons compound, Number 20223 of 1934, made specially for Mrs A. Deakin and Sons, Brynmar, Brecon, who used it on their dodgems ride machine. 'Supreme' served for only six years in showland work before being commandeered in 1940, to carry out bomb damage demolition and heavy haulage. After a series of owners and a deteriorating state of repair, 'Supreme' was bought by Jack Wharton of Minster Lovell, Oxfordshire, and taken to his mechanical and electrical engineering works, where restoration work was begun. Under Jack's watchful eye and with a volunteer team who spent twenty thousand hours on the task, twelve years of work brought 'Supreme' to its present state. Running light, the engine can cover 20-25 miles (32-40 km) between water stops, burns a hundredweight of coal every 8 miles (50 kg every 13 km) and obtains her power from two 12 inch (305 mm) stroke cylinders, of 7 inches (178 mm) and 12 inches respectively, using 200 pounds per square inch steam pressure. The maximum indicated rating was 125 horsepower.*

An Aveling and Porter of Rochester single-cylinder 'agricultural locomotive' of about 1875, specially adapted for pushing a corn reaper. The sprocket on the flywheel transmitted, through the long roller chain, power for rotating the sails and the reciprocating knife that cut the standing grain. A second chain, wound round the rear axle winding drum and passing up the crane jib, was used to raise the reaper from the ground whilst reversing at corners for the next cut. The notion of pushing instead of pulling a reaper was not original; in the ancient world Gaulish farmers hitched their oxen to primitive corn cutters in this way. A heavy cumbersome traction engine, however well handled, could never have succeeded with a reaper, whether fore or aft. Horses did the work far better and it was not until the 1930s that the motor tractor ousted them from this harvesting activity.

This fearful accident of 15th January 1873 killed three men: George Reene, the driver; William Bird, the stoker; and William Darling, who was joy-riding on the drawbar between engine and threshing machine. The badly injured and scalded enginemen were rescued from drowning but died within a few hours. Darling, trapped underwater, was drowned. Edward Butler, the steersman on the forecarriage, and the man sitting beside him were fortunately thrown clear uninjured. The fifty-year-old Broadmead Bridge, owned by the fourth Earl of Onslow, spanned the river Wey at Old Woking, Surrey, on the present-day A247. Its timber piles were so badly rotted away at water level that a civil engineer told the coroner the bridge was unsafe for a horse-drawn load of corn. Although Reene was foolhardy to attempt the passage with his 10 ton engine, he probably knew that a local farmer named Hilder had got over the bridge with his 12 ton traction engine seven weeks earlier. The tackle was owned by Thomas Miskin, a farmer and contractor of Hersham and Walton nearby. The engine was a Clayton and Shuttleworth of Lincoln twin-cylinder single expansion type, either Number 8263 or 8678, both sold new to him in 1868. This style of agricultural engine marks the period when tractions began to supersede portables on farms.

HISTORICAL BACKGROUND

The traction engine originated because there was a need for mechanical power to pull loads, especially threshing machines, on the public roads of Britain. During the eighteenth century the steam engine had been slowly improved from a crude type of engine that could push the plunger of a mine water pump up and down into one that could turn a wheel. From 1800 onwards British engineers gave much thought to adapting these steam engines for road transport. The basic parts of the simple steam engine available to these pioneers were: a round iron boiler in which the invisible gas called steam was generated; a cylinder having inside it a piston which the steam pushed backwards and forwards; and a crank which made a wheel go round.

George Stephenson's *Rocket* of 1829 established the steam locomotive on the railways. Although Stephenson's fame rests upon his locomotives, he did consider the possibility of some form of traction engine and the development of road haulage, before deciding on railway transport. The road users, however, could not copy the railway engine, simply because it was a one-gear machine with its driving wheels coupled directly to the pistons. There were steep and unalterable gradients on the roads, surmountable only by geared machines.

The traction engine as we know it was evolved from an experiment made in 1859, when Aveling and Porter of Rochester changed a Clayton and Shuttleworth of Lincoln portable engine, which needed horses to pull it from one job to the next, into a self-moving one.

This pre-1897 photograph, taken in Kent, shows 14 nhp Fowler plough engine Number 1238 of 1869, which had two 8 inch (203 mm) diameter simple expansion cylinders, a low boiler pressure of only 100 pounds, and was known as a horizontal shaft type, from the horizontal shaft between crankshaft and the upright shaft that drove the rope drum. This engine, along with its mate Number 1250, was supplied new to Mr William Levett's Staplehurst Steam Ploughing Company, of Cranbrook, Kent. Many of this type, probably the first practical two-engine style cultivation engines, were built during the late 1860s at Leeds. The hind wheel master spoke (seen at the 'two o'clock' position) is part of the friction grip drive between the rear axle and the wheel itself. There is a boiler feed pump below the crankshaft, although on later engines pumps were replaced by a second injector allowing drivers to fill their boilers during the idle periods when the other engine was pulling back the implement, when no crankshaft rotation was available to drive a pump.

This was done by fitting a long driving chain between the crankshaft and the rear axle. From this modification came the spate of traction engine building of the next decade.

Traction engines were made in works large and small throughout England. There were a few Scottish builders, but none in either Wales or Ireland. Small concerns made one or two engines, whilst big undertakings such as John Fowler of Leeds, Charles Burrell of Thetford or Aveling and Porter of Rochester each made thousands of them. At the height of the business there were some ninety firms in the trade. The engines were more or less hand-made by cunning craftsmen. Some firms, like Burrells, went so far to suit their customers' precise requirements that no two of their engines were turned out exactly alike.

The heyday of traction engine building extended over the sixty years from 1860 to 1920. A rapid decline in orders set in after 1920, a result of the successful development of the internal combustion engined tractor during the First World War. By 1925 it was clear that the day of the traction engine was over. Some firms like Burrells later went bankrupt, while others soon decided that they must seek a new line of business or close. There was very little steam engine construction after 1936. The last engine of all, an Aveling-Barford steam roller, was built in 1950, when the Grantham firm subcontracted the work to Vickers-Armstrong of Newcastle upon Tyne.

4

ABOVE: *J. and F. Howard, Britannia Works, Bedford, built unorthodox engines, of which the 'Farmer's Friend' is one of the less unusual. Made in 1877, this one-engine ploughing outfit worked for over fifty years for Mr R. Stephenson of Burwell in Cambridgeshire. Taken in the 1920s, this photograph shows the tackle travelling with the self-moving anchor cart that stood on the opposite side of the field to the engine, followed by the three-wheeled cultivator and balanced plough. The single cylinder, motionwork and crankshaft are, Howard style, all placed in the bunker beside the driver. The rope of the horizontally hung winding drum, rear of the bunker, is led forward under the engine to the paying-out sheave wheel seen below the front toolbox. This engine was finally scrapped during the Second World War.*

BELOW: *Foundrymen, smiths and engine fitters at the Tortington Ironworks, Arundel, West Sussex, about 1880. The flint-faced octagonal blacksmith's shop in the background (still standing) was formerly an oil mill where a horse paced round and round providing the power to grind oil seed into flour. Sleeveless waistcoats are a favourite outer garment, whilst bowler hats had not then become the distinguishing head-dress of foremen. These were the days before engineering workmen had overalls or boiler suits as protective clothing. In addition to general agricultural engineering, James Penfold undertook much steam work here.*

ABOVE: *The stand of Richard Garrett and Sons of Leiston, Suffolk, at the Great Exhibition of 1851 in Hyde Park. Unusual features on this very early portable engine are a steam dome over the firebox, crankshaft in front of the smokebox, and turning carriage under the round-bottomed firebox. The outsize flywheel matched a slow-running engine with the thousand revolutions per minute beater drum required for a threshing machine. Like all engines of its day, this had a boiler made of wrought iron, prone to rust corrosion and fractures between rivet holes. An attractive engine, ingeniously constructed and interesting in many ways, this was an outstanding piece of farm steam machinery at the beginning of the 1850s. The horse-drawn implements are: left, a seed drill; right, a cultivator.*

BELOW: *This Savages Ltd, of King's Lynn, Norfolk, 'Sea-on-Land' revolving amusement machine of the late nineteenth century was driven by a centrally placed portable engine. The smaller flywheel on the engine belongs to the separate and tiny organ engine, which had a 3 by 4 inch (76 by 101 mm) single cylinder, and ran continuously during opening times. Power from the portable, taken upwards on a mitre-wheeled shaft to the overhead rotating framework, flung the six yachts along their circular and gyratory courses.*

This Locomobile threshing engine was made in the 1890s by the Aultman and Taylor Machinery Company, Mansfield, Ohio, USA. Although self-propelled, on long journeys, with the boiler emptied to reduce weight, it was horse-drawn. The engine's large-diameter return-tube boiler was fired with straw fed into the firehold below the chimney. The engineer's platform under the steering wheel is placed so the regulator valve is in front and the reverser on the right. A domed boiler, disc crank, grease lubrication and lightweight steel-rod spokes in the road wheels are typical American features. Fuel economy was achieved by passing exhaust steam through the rectangular feed water heater below the single cylinder.

THE PORTABLE ENGINE

Portable engines were the predecessors of the traction engine. They were early small steam engines without road wheels, but which could be carried from place to place on their wooden frames. From about 1840 portable engines, now mounted on free-running road wheels and pulled about by a team of three or four horses, became common on farms for use with threshing machines. The portable was a very simple engine consisting of little more than a boiler with its feed pump, long chimney, cylinder and connecting rod, crankshaft, valve gear, flywheel and three or four other mountings, such as a pressure gauge and glass tube water-level indicator.

The portable engine's power was transferred by a long leather belt from its large flywheel to the machinery it drove, usually a threshing machine or the circular saw in a sawmill. These engines were lovely to look at whilst at work and their sound was soothing, as they rocked gently to and fro against the wooden chocks on either side of their hind wheels.

The great majority of portable engines had their cylinder fixed on top of the firebox at the rear end of the boiler, with crankshaft and flywheel at the front or chimney end. This order was reversed on the new traction engines, bringing the crankshaft into a handy position for connecting it, by toothed gear wheels, to the hind or driving axle. With this arrangement, if the driver found his engine stuck on dead centre (a piston at either end of the cylinder), he could reach out from his manstand and pull the flywheel to reposition the piston for a start.

The coming of the traction engine, however, did not put the portable out of business, and such engines continued at work well into the 1930s. Furthermore, portables were being built twenty years after the traction engine trade had ended. Robey of Lincoln, a big firm in its day, was making portables, mostly for export, up to the early 1950s.

ABOVE: Chimney smoke drifts gently away from this Penfold-owned Charles Burrell of Thetford 6 nhp single-crank compound, Number 3665 of 1915, threshing at Bignor, West Sussex, in 1948. These compounds, with their high-pressure cylinder over the low, and both piston rods coupled to one large crosshead block, were favourites with many drivers. The late model threshing machine, made by Clayton and Shuttleworth of Lincoln, had a 4 foot 6 inch (1.37 m) long beater drum, as well as a pipe through which the chaff was blown away at middle left. It was usual for farmers to hire sacks for threshing and in this instance they belong to the Bristol-based West of England Sack Company, a subsidiary of the former Great Western Railway.

BELOW: The sale on 5th August 1948 at J. G. Jackson and Son, threshing contractors of Ramsey Heights, Cambridgeshire. The five single-cylinder engines are: first and fifth from camera, Wallis and Steevens of Basingstoke, second and fourth Fowells of nearby St Ives, and the third in line was an 8 nhp Foster of Lincoln. All the engines were bought, for only a few pounds each, for scrap in Sheffield while local farmers bought the drums, elevators and straw balers for further use.

This beautifully restored working exhibit from the Museum of East Anglian Life, Stowmarket, is a 1912 Burrell single-crank compound, Number 3399, 'Empress of Britain'. The photograph shows clearly Burrell's diagonal arrangement of the two cylinders with high pressure at top and low pressure below. After beginning her working life hauling timber and roadstone at Mattishall in Norfolk, Number 3399 was eventually used mainly for threshing. Thomas Gasgoigne of Bodicote, Oxfordshire, bought the engine in 1977 from metal merchants J. W. Hardwick of West Ewell, and commenced restoration. In 1983 'Empress of Britain' was acquired by the museum, from which she often goes to rallies within a 20 to 30 mile (32 to 48 km) radius.

THE GENERAL PURPOSE ENGINE

The general purpose engine was a simple, usually single-cylinder traction engine used mainly in agriculture. It was a cheap and straightforward engine built with no frills or adornments in order to keep the selling price to a minimum. General purpose engines were essentially threshing engines, owned mostly by threshing contractors who toured the farms in autumn, winter and early spring. The outfit consisted, in addition to the engine, of a threshing drum, a straw elevator and sometimes a chaff cutter as well. The contractor supplied the tackle, together with an engine driver and a man to feed the drum. During the middle 1920s, a time of trade depression and low costs, the contractor charged about £3 a day for his machine and men. The farmer would provide the coal and cart the water, as well as supply the remainder of the general labour. After about 1925,

motor tractors began to oust the traction engine from its traditional job of driving the threshing machinery and, to the onlooker, threshing was never the same again.

After the general purpose engine had become established on agricultural duties, use for it was soon found performing road haulage work with loads of stone, bricks, manure, coal, timber or general merchandise, often over fairly long distances. Even those engines used mainly for threshing were, in the non-threshing months of May, June and July, often put to work before a saw bench. When a traction engine was 'on the belt', as they said, it was essential that its speed was maintained at a uniform rate. For this purpose a governor was fitted over the motionwork at the cylinder end. Early engines had the James Watt type two-ball governor, whilst later ones were

9

equipped with Pickering style governors having three smaller rotating balls. The latter, with their spring-cushioned control rods, were preferred on account of their more sensitive control. In practice, the driver set his governor for the desired speed, opened the regulator into the full steam on position and then left it to the governor to take control. As the load on the engine varied according to the volume of unthreshed grain fed into the drum of a threshing job, or the size of log placed upon a saw bench, the governors were constantly in action on a working engine.

Operators seem to have preferred single-cylinder general purpose engines to compounds, which, it was often alleged, governed badly. General purpose engines were the most numerous of all tractions, a fact that supports the assertion that traction engines were primarily agricultural machines.

General purpose engines, like all other traction engines (except steam rollers, which are classified by their weight) have their power rating expressed as so many nominal horsepower (nhp). This misleading term puzzles many people for it is well below the actual indicated horsepower. In the early days, when there was much opposition to the use of steam engines on the roads, it was considered less likely to arouse antagonism in county councils if an understatement was made concerning the size of the next engine to appear. There was a formula for determining nhp, but multiplying the stated figure by eight will produce a fair approximation of the actual horsepower of any engine.

Richard Hornsby of Grantham, former village blacksmith at nearby Barrowby, made his first portable in 1849. The firm made its last steam engine of any kind in 1906. Seen here in 1933, when it was owned by Clark Brothers of Bilsington, Kent, is single-cylinder Hornsby and Sons 6 nhp Number 7298 of 1891, a general purpose engine, with a Hornsby threshing machine. An unusual feature is the separate steam circuit associated with the speed governor, placed under the control of the driver by means of a long rod reaching back to the manstand. Originally this engine had a two-ball Watt-type governor fitted beside the slide bars, but this has been replaced by a Pickering governor of more sensitive control. Wheel slip and bogging down experienced with engines of this type led Hornsbys to experiment with tracked vehicles around the end of the nineteenth century, a revolutionary move that was to make possible the British army tanks of the First World War.

ABOVE: *Named 'Excelsior', this neat and business-like engine is an 'Economic' type 8 nhp general purpose engine, Number 352, made in 1893 by William Tasker and Sons, Waterloo Works, Andover, Hampshire. Steam to the single cylinder — 9½ inch (241 mm) bore and 12¼ inch (311 mm) stroke — was distributed through a slide valve by the cylinder side. Advertised features were: a Tasker-made safety valve, an eccentric-driven boiler water feed pump, an injector, and a cable drum on the rear axle left-hand side. Extra braking power was found in a hand-operated brake that acted on a motion spur wheel. 'Excelsior' was a three-shaft engine, meaning that power was transmitted through a train of three rotating shafts: crankshaft, intermediate shaft and rear axle. The flywheel on three-shaft engines turns forwards when travelling ahead, and the reverse applies to four-shaft engines. Three-shaft engines, with one less shaft to consume part of their power, generally had a slightly higher mechanical efficiency than four-shaft engines.*

RIGHT: *This 6 nhp traction engine, made in the 1880s by William Weeks and Son, a small builder who operated from the Perseverance Works at Maidstone, Kent, had finished its working life by the time this photograph was taken in the 1930s. Unusually for a British engine, the front wheels are spoked with wrought iron round rod. The wooden plank sidewalk, by this time very dilapidated and unsafe, gave the driver access for examining and oiling the motion-work.*

ABOVE: *Aveling and Porter steam roller Number 2958 of 1892 at work in Austria, 1948, whilst owned by Messrs Stuag, road-making and rolling contractors. Originally a 12 ton crane-fitted 8 nhp traction engine, this overhead slide valve compound was sold new to the Swiss Military Department, which used it for hauling field guns. It was later used as a mobile electricity generator by the Kludsky Circus. In 1912 the makers supplied a new 'combined-engine saddle' and steerage fork when conversion to a roller was undertaken in Austria, as seen in this photograph. In 1942 the roller was commandeered for war work with the German Todt Organisation. In December 1966 this much travelled and modified engine was scrapped in Austria.*

BELOW: *In addition to making Number 12045, seen here in 1955, Aveling and Porter of Rochester, Kent, built some 8,600 other rollers, making them the largest and best known of British steam roller makers. This engine, owned and operated by Fife County Council, Kirkcaldy District Committee, spent its life in Scotland. Standing with the engine is the late William Oswald of Kirkcaldy.*

12

The author's Fowler 12 ton 1927 steam roller Number 17077 picking up water from the river Wye at High Wycombe, Buckinghamshire, August Bank Holiday Monday, 1965. Those who have driven steam engines over British roads appreciate coming across a river of good, clean flowing water within reach of the pick-up pipe. Unusually for a roller, Number 17077 had two rows of spokes and two T rings in her hind wheels, as well as a B6 road locomotive cylinder block. These features may indicate that, as some said, the engine was originally intended as a road locomotive. Engine and van, bought in 1961 from the Mechanical Tar and Grouting Company of Reading for £125, were sold in 1979 for £3,700.

THE STEAM ROLLER

Although their main purpose was not to pull loads on roads, both steam rollers and steam ploughs are regarded as traction engines. Rollers were seen by the public more frequently than any other type of road engine, for as the maker and repairer of roads it found its way into every hamlet, village, town and city in the land. They were made in 6, 8, 10, 12 and even 15 ton sizes and everywhere these useful steam machines transformed the former rough-surfaced roads into smooth stone-free highways. Their drivers kept them in a clean and polished condition, making them all the more attractive to look at.

The first steam roller was made in 1866. Before that horses had pulled heavy rollers to consolidate the surfaces of new roads. Once the traction engine had become established, the next step was to put a steam engine over the heavy rolls. With the exception of modern motorways, British roads owe their foundation work to the steam roller. Most rollers had cabs that kept rain off the driver and generally the make of engine could be determined at a distance by the shape and style of its cab. Nearly all rollers had block-type flywheels. Many were fitted with scarifiers, hung behind the offside rear roll for the purpose of breaking up the old surface before laying a new one over it. When the scarifier was in action it presented steam rollers with the hardest of all their pulling jobs.

Most steam rollers were either operated by contractors on hire to town or county councils or owned and used by the councils themselves. Most traction engine building firms made some steam rollers, but Aveling and Porter were the biggest manufacturers: of the 12,700 steam engines they made, no less than 8,600 were steam rollers. The Kentish rampant horse and *Invicta* symbol, in brightly polished brass, adorned the front end of every one of their rollers. Aveling and Porter rollers looked good and were quiet runners but they lacked the sturdiness of those made by builders such as Fowlers of Leeds, Marshalls of Gainsborough or Burrells of Thetford. For all that, the Rochester engines were favourites with purchasers, in Britain and elsewhere.

The ordinary motor driving licence, whilst covering heavy and light traction engines, is no authority to drive a steam roller. 'L' plates and a subsequent driving test are the preliminaries to having steam roller authority included on a motor driving licence. But rollers, regarded as road-making machinery, are exempt from road fund licences. Steam rollers, never regarded as 'classy' machines by enthusiasts, are the cheapest form of traction engine on the market. Rollers lasted longer in commercial use than any other form of engine. Some were still at work in the late 1970s.

This photograph, taken in preservation days, shows a 17 ton, 65 bhp William Foster of Lincoln showman's engine, Number 14446 'The Leader' of 1921, which had a long working life with Pat Collins and Company, amusement caterers of Bloxwich. As late as October 1956 this engine, driven by showland veteran Jim Morley, was performing with a set of gondolas at the Nottingham Goose Fair. Foster's showmen's engines were not only attractive, they were also first-class road runners, capable of 15 - 20 mph (24 - 32 km per hour), and could withstand a lot of punishment. The belt-driven main dynamo ahead of the chimney had its magnetic field strengthened by current from the smaller dynamo, known as an exciter, behind the chimney.

Lowland Scotland was famous for its fairs and the amusement caterers who toured them with steam-powered machinery. This is Bill Bastable's Burrell 8 nhp showman's three-speed engine, Number 3279 of 1911, 'Prince Albert', at Candlerigg's fairground in April 1940 with one wagon of her dodgems hooked on behind ready for departure to the next 'pitch' at Hamilton. Originally built for Jacob Studt senior of Maesteg, Number 3279 afterwards passed through the hands of several owners before going to Bastables at Stirling. Scottish showmen's engines ran fairly long distances over more hilly country than English engines encountered, making their lives much harder.

THE SHOWMAN'S ENGINE

The showman's engine is the aristocrat of the traction engine world. Its gay paintwork, polished brass and scrolled decorations never fail to win admiration. It is also the most sought after by moneyed preservationists. Mechanically, these engines are more or less ordinary road locomotives, well dressed up on the outside.

Travelling showmen, or amusement caterers, were often colourful characters, vying with each other in having the most striking and most magnificent engine with their name painted on the side boards of its cab. Both builders and purchasers were lavish in their use of decorative copper and brass. Twisted brass sheathed the cab support columns, great polished brass stars brightened the side motion plates, big copper or brass caps enclosed the road wheel hubs, whilst the cylinder sides were cased in mirror-bright sheet brass or copper. The painters, too, spared no effort, turning out the wheels in yellow and every conceivable variation in the lining out of the general paintwork.

Eleven British firms, between the years 1885 and 1934, made a total of 411 showman's engines, as follows: Charles Burrell of Thetford, 207; John Fowler of Leeds, 82; William Foster of Lincoln, 68; J. and H. MacLaren of Leeds, 16; Wallis and Steevens of Basingstoke, 13; Fodens of Sandbach, 10; Richard Garrett of Leiston, 5; Savage Brothers of King's Lynn, 5; Aveling and Porter of Rochester, 2; Ransomes of Ipswich, 2; Richard Hornsby of Grantham, 1. Fowlers made the first one and Fosters the last, *Princess Marina*, which was sold in 1934 to Mr. T. Drakeley of Stechford, Birmingham. Additionally, a number of ordinary road locomotives have, during preservation days, been converted into showman's type, as has an occasional steam roller.

The showman's engine was a dual purpose machine, serving as a mobile electricity generator at the fair and then hauling a load of amusement machinery to the next site. The belt-driven dynamo in front of the chimney provided power for lighting or turning the various 'rides' such as roundabouts, cake walks, gondolas and dodgems. In order to increase the output of the dynamo, especially to feed the power-hungry scenic railway machines, a second and smaller dynamo was fitted between the chimney and cylinder block. Known as an exciter, its job was to send a separate flow of current over the magnets of the main dynamo, increasing its output accordingly. All showman's engines had full-length canopies and block-style flywheels. When generating at fairgrounds, the engine speed, held constant by governors, was around 200 revolutions per minute. Names were necessary for these magnificent engines and their wide variety was amazing: *Her Majesty, Ex Mayor, Prince Bert, The Pride of North Wales, The White Rose of York, Victory, Duchess of Northumberland, Little Alf* and *Supreme* are examples.

One of the great spectacles of Britain's steam age days was the sight of two or more showman's engines standing side by side generating electricity on their pitch at a fairground. Often these fairs, held by right of ancient charters, were on paved and cambered roads in town high streets. As the engines required a level stance, their drivers used to pack them up level on wooden blocks and there they stood pulsating away in all their glory amid the low thunder of their rotating motionwork, with the music from the organs in the background blaring out the popular tunes of the day.

In spite of their grand appearance, showman's engines were hard-worked machines. At the fair they had to provide electrical power for the amusement machines and as soon as one fair finished, usually about midnight, they had to prepare to move on to the next one. Drivers usually slept for a short time while the general hands took down the rides, but they were ready to take the road again between six or eight in the morning. Tommy Glover of Witchford, Cambridgeshire, once drove Green Brothers of Preston 7 nhp Burrell showman's engine Number 3089 *His Majesty*, with a load of around 30 tons, the 241 miles (388 km) from Stamford Fair to Exeter in a running time of forty-two hours extending over three and a half days. Even after a run like that there would be no respite for engine or man, as the fair was on again the next day. These engines had three-speed gears, slow, intermediate and fast, in order that drivers could take adantage of the ups, downs and levels of the winding roads. Water was picked up, roughly every 10 miles (16 km), from wayside ponds, streams or rivers, whilst coal was purchased from any convenient coal merchant the crews passed during their journeys.

Named 'Enterprise', this engine was designed by Savages around 1890 in an attempt to combine a centre engine and traction engine in one machine. By removing the top section of the chimney, and then diverting the smoke into a central flue, the radius arms of the roundabouts were given a clear field of rotation. This innovation, however, never became popular with showmen, who preferred the later truck-mounted twin-cylinder (5 inch, 127 mm, bore and 9 inch, 229 mm, stroke) silent-running centre engines of lightweight design.

Penfold's yard at Arundel, West Sussex, in 1915. A Fowler 14 nhp plough engine of the 1870s shows off her new boiler and longer smokebox made and fitted by the Oxford Steam Plough Company, Cowley, Oxford. When Fowler plough engines needed new boilers, many owners preferred Oxford to Leeds for rebuilding. Oxford boilers had fifty-five 2 inch (51 mm) tubes and boiler plate 7/16 inch (11 mm) thick that permitted the boiler pressure to be raised to 160 pounds per square inch. These modified engines were very popular with many owners, one of whom testified in a letter to the Oxford company how the slightly larger tubes not only improved the steaming, but that each engine also burnt 5 hundredweight (254 kg) less coal daily. Appearance at the front end also benefited from the repositioned front axle sitting under, rather than ahead of, the smokebox. This engine has a Penfold-fitted flywheel rim hand brake that gave peace of mind to drivers descending steep hills. The original tank steerage with its 'turn left to go right' peculiarity has been retained, as well as the Fowler cylinder block with its single 11 inch (280 mm) bore and 12 inch (305 mm) stroke cylinder.

THE STEAM PLOUGH ENGINE

Because the steam plough was an agricultural engine, spending most of its working life in remote fields, it is not as well known as it should be. Steam ploughs are the largest and most powerful of all traction engines: the biggest of them weighed almost 25 tons and were rated at 275 indicated horsepower. No other engine so impressively demonstrates the immense power of steam.

Several methods of steam cultivation were tried in Britain, but it was only the system with two engines using steel cable, introduced by John Fowler, a Quaker, in 1861, that proved successful in Britain or on the European mainland. The pioneers of 1850-60 were very disappointed when they realised that traction type engines were far too heavy in relation to their power output to pull implements behind them, for they wasted almost all their available power upon pulling themselves along on the land.

For the ten years following 1850 steam cultivation was therefore undertaken by stationary portable engines. The engine stood in one corner of the field, where it drove, by belt, a two-way winding winch, from which an iron wire rope was led round the field and so drew the imple-

ABOVE: *Tea-break during summer cultivating in Sussex in the 1920s, using a Penfolds of Arundel 8 nhp single-cylinder plough engine known as one of the 'Fowler late eights'. Following the introduction of compound plough engines in 1881, Fowlers discontinued single-cylindered types. However, a small market arose in the mid 1880s among purchasers who could afford only cheap tackle, so a further batch of these small engines was made at Leeds. They had an 8½ inch (216 mm) bore and 12 inch (305 mm) stroke cylinder supplied with steam at 140 pounds pressure. Cultivating was rough but healthy work which the gangs carried out in two separate operations, done and crossed, that is, the implement was taken crosswise across the field a second time in order to tear out any deep rooting weeds like docks or thistles missed the first time over.*

BELOW: *19 ton, 1918 Fowler 16 nhp BB class compound engine, Number 15167 or 15221, attached by cable to a mole plough during the laying of an underground water supply to the Duke of Norfolk's farm at Michelgrove, West Sussex. This rather unusual steam job of the early 1930s was done before water authorities provided a piped water supply to many outlying farms. When summer droughts dried up the ponds from which the animals drank, farmers were put to much expense carting water for their sheep, horses and cattle, hence this private enterprise project. This engine, along with her three Arundel sisters, worked during the Second World War on the historic 'PLUTO' (Pipe Line Under The Ocean) through which petrol was pumped to France in 1944 for the invading 'D' Day allied armies. Duke and Ockenden were the water supply contractors.*

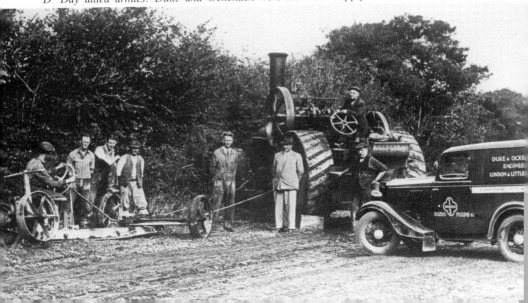

Fowler B4 compound 12 nhp plough engine Number 12407, 'Napoleon', new in 1914, owned by A. R. Oliver, steam work contractors of Wandon End, Luton, on cultivation work in the early 1920s. This attractive engine is of advanced design for 1914. The two bright steel levers pointing upwards to the driver, W. Woods, indicate that this engine had two-speed ploughing gear. The 450 yard (411 m) long cable did not reach from hedge to hedge in this particular field, so the engine was working across the middle of it. Behind the driver is G. Harris and, on the ground from left to right, are W. Woodcock, F. Lee and E. Bray. Olivers, still in business as agricultural contractors and salesmen, long since finished with steam power of any kind.

ment to and fro. From 1861, the introduction of two-engine traction-type tackles, with winding drums slung under the engine's boilers, quickly led to the popularity of steam on land cultivation. Whilst many firms, large and small, had made the portables that undertook the first steam work, only five firms manufactured traction engine style plough engines. They were Charles Burrell of Thetford, Aveling and Porter of Rochester, J. and H. McLaren and John Fowler, both of Leeds and John Allen of Oxford. Fowlers were the principal makers, far outstripping any of the other four. Of the two engines in a steam plough tackle, one was constructed for pulling its cable on its right-hand side, the other for pulling it on its left. They were known as right and left hand engines respectively, although their positions in the field were the reverse.

The first big challenge to the steam plough came during the First World War, when American-built motor tractors, often handled by soldiers in uniform, were sent by agricultural committees on contract hire to farmers as part of a campaign for increased food production. After the war, many farmers bought their own tractors, and by the middle 1920s they did not need to hire the steam tackle, except for ploughing the heaviest clay land. By 1930 it was realised that, with the rising cost of coal and its labour-intensive machinery, steam could not compete with petrol-paraffin tractors that ploughed an acre on 1½ gallons of fuel (17 litres per hectare) and were handled by one man only, against four men and a cookboy on the steam tackles. Both fuel and labour costs for the steam tackle were six or seven times greater than for the tractor. Ward and Dale, the largest of the steam cultivation contractors, with twenty-five sets based on their depot at Sleaford, Lincolnshire, sold out completely in March 1939.

At the height of the steam plough's popularity in 1918 there were some 650 two-engined tackles at work in Great Britain, of which 107 were in Lincolnshire. There are about 170 steam ploughs preserved in Britain, most of them in a workable condition. About a dozen farmer owners do some steam ploughing or cultivating once a year whilst others engage in contract work dredging out large ponds and lakes.

ABOVE: *Fowler BB1 compound 16 nhp plough engine, probably Number 15220, sold new to Penfolds in 1918, ready for Nigeria in 1951. Following work on the 'PLUTO' pipeline in the Second World War, this engine was overhauled at Tortington Ironworks, Arundel, and, with her sister engines, Numbers 15221 and 15166/67, was sold to the Colonial Development Corporation for a native resettlement scheme. They were eventually scrapped in Africa. The BB class was popular for British farmwork and was sold in two models, the BB 14 nhp and the BB1 16 nhp. The additional 2 nhp was gained by increasing the high-pressure bore by 1/4 inch (6 mm) and the low by 1/2 inch (13 mm). The tall man is Frank Penfold.*

BELOW: *Engineer Julius Kemna's Steam Plough Works, Breslau, Germany, made this 1926 Type EZN plough engine. After Britain, the next best place in which to find first-class cable-style plough engines was Germany. This engine has a smoketube-located superheater for delivering high-temperature steam to the two single-expansion cylinders and only one underslung slide bar for each piston rod crosshead. The steerage gear is hung on the underside of the boiler barrel.*

ABOVE: *A French traction engine of about 1910, made by the Societe Francais of Vierzon (Cher), for threshing and other purposes. Steam admission and exhaust were effected by double-beat poppet style valves which were driven from a Stephenson link-motion valve gear. Whilst threshing, the Pickering-type governor held the engine at 240 revolutions per minute on a 20 to 25 horsepower rating. Note how the cylinder assembly is held aloft clear of the boiler barrel on a slender bracket.*

BELOW: *This fine American farm engine was built by the Avery Company of Peoria in Illinois around 1910. It is an under-mounted type with twin cylinders under its boiler, railway locomotive style. Used mainly for direct ploughing or for autumn threshing, American steam engines were, as in Britain, quickly ousted during the 1920s by motor tractors.*

ABOVE: *Unexpected disaster overtook this Fowler 14 ton, 12 nhp KKS (superheated) Number 13422 plough engine 'Sunshine' on 1st June, 1959, only 300 yards from its home, the rectory at Tacolneston, Norfolk, while en route to the nearby Woodton rally. The late Reverend R. C. Stebbing, on the right, its driver and owner, was the acknowledged expert on mechanical matters relating to Fowler plough engines. The rear axle had broken and, following police anxiety about blockage of the highway, the scrapman was called in.*

BELOW: *This photograph, taken on 3rd April 1984 at Emsworth on the land side of Thorney Island, West Sussex, shows the 18 nhp AA6 Fowler plough engine Number 13877, built in 1917, dredging new pools for wildfowl on marshland under the sea bank. Alan Pronger of Trotton near Midhurst drives the engine, which has 600 yards (549 m) of discarded colliery winding rope wound round its cable drum. Alan's son Michael was on BB 14213 of 1914, the pulling-back engine standing 500 yards (457 m) away across the rough grass and reed-strewn marshland. Bogged-down engines are a risk on all dredging work, hence the formidable array of spuds, or wheel grips, hanging over the bunker end.*

22

Tasker 5 nhp steam tractor Number 1741 of 1917 as seen prior to the liquidation sale of 22nd February 1969, when the engine was sold for £1,800 to Messrs Hardwicke, the Ewell scrap iron merchants, and preserved by them. These three-speed, roller chain drive B2 compound 'Little Giant' tractors were quiet and fast running, popular with both owners and drivers. The 5 inch (127 mm) by 7¾ inch (197 mm) bore and 8 inch (203 mm) stroke cylinders had overhead slide valves and the cylinder block was lubricated by displacement style lubricators that functioned on the principle that water, slowly condensed from a top steam supply, displaced the oil along a small-bore pipe leading to the block. Good braking power, essential for these 15 mph (24 km/h) runners, was provided in the form of both flywheel and rear axle hand brakes. For replenishing the boiler, there was a choice of two injectors, whilst the fully sprung engine gave the crew a smooth ride.

THE LIGHT STEAM TRACTOR

Light steam tractors are the smallest of British traction engines. Some of them weighed only 3 tons, and the largest did not exceed 7¼ tons. Introduction of these lightweight and fast steam tractors came about as a result of a change in the laws. Until 1903 the speed of all traction engines was limited to 2 miles (3 km) per hour whilst passing through villages or towns and 4 miles (6 km) per hour on the open road. In spite of much complaint about this unfair restriction, both the government and the county councils were strongly opposed to any relaxations that would encourage the unwanted traction engine. It was the coming of motor cars and light lorries around 1900 that brought a change in the permitted road speed regulations. Motors could not be restricted to low speeds, neither could the steam operators be denied a slight improvement. The Heavy Motor Cars Orders of 1903 laid down that a light traction engine, weighing not more than 5 tons, might travel at 5 miles (8 km) an hour and could be handled by one man only, instead of two. These concessions, although small, encouraged many makers to begin production of light steam tractors. Practically every large firm began to make its own line of lightweight steamer and there was a reasonably brisk market for them amongst furniture hauliers, timber merchants and general road hauliers,

ABOVE: *The 1903 send-off for a vertical-boilered Wantage Engineering Company built steam wagon, owned by Mr William Keen, furniture manfacturer, of High Wycombe, Buckinghamshire, on its maiden trip with seven hundred chairs for London. This 8 miles (13 km) an hour road steamer easily outpaced horse-drawn wagons and could make the 60 miles (97 km) round trip in a day. Large lumps of coal are stacked on the bunker, left side, at hand for recharging the furnace. Two or three times on each run water would be taken on, by means of a flexible suction pipe, from wayside ponds or streams. During stops, any clinker on the firebars could be removed through the iron door below the registration number plate.*

BELOW: *This motley assembly of traction engines, rollers and steam wagons was testing the then longest British concrete span of 180 feet (55 m) on the 1923 Thames bridge at Reading. Instruments, carried on the moored barge below, showed that the 372 tons load imposed a mere ¾ inch (19 mm) deflection of the arch. The roller bringing up the rear was Wallis and Steevens Number 7329 of 1913, owned by Ford and Son, the well known road rolling contractors of Wokingham in Berkshire.*

who carried merchandise such as bricks, road stone or whatever loads were offered to them. It was the first attempt to meet competition from the developing motor vehicle. At first most of these smaller and faster engines were single-cylinder models but compounds later became almost universal.

The Heavy Motor Cars Act of 1923 increased the permitted weight of steam motor tractors to 7¼ tons, allowing a heavier and more powerful engine to run at 5 miles (8 km) per hour. Introduced at a time when the much faster motor lorry already had a good proportion of road traffic, this relaxation gave only marginal benefit, for the motor lorry's inroads could not be halted.

Steam tractors were capable of hauling an 8 ton load 10 miles (16 km) on a hundredweight of coal, with 30 mile (48 km) runs between water stops. By 1930 village policemen, now well accustomed to 50 miles per hour (80 km/h) motor traffic, left off trying to catch a 'speeding' traction engine driver, with the result that the drivers of many a light steam tractor, on rubber tyres, cruised at up to 20 miles per hour (32 km/h).

THE ROAD LOCOMOTIVE

The road locomotive, a comparatively heavy and powerful machine, was used primarily for pulling big and important loads on the roads. In their day, these splendid traction engines hauled such interesting loads as ship's propellers or rudders, very heavy blocks of building stone carried in four-wheeled trucks, railway locomotives between works and docks for export, bricks and tiles, timber and lumber or, towards the end of their time, electrical transformers and so on. The nature of their work called for the most experienced of drivers.

Mechanically, these engines were a larger and improved version of the general purpose engine used in agriculture, with a few extra items such as a good

Testing the new Briardale Road bridge in Liverpool, 12th November 1926, with two Fowler crane-fitted compound-type road locomotives, each hauling a 25 ton trailer. The helmeted traffic control policeman watches whilst city engineers check for any visible deflections under the 90 tons test load. Owned by George Watson and Company of Liverpool, the engine on the left is B5 class Number 9983, new to them in June 1904. By 1921 it was in the possession of Edward Box, and in 1947 it was in the hands of J. Routledge. On the right is class A4, Number 9516, supplied new on 30th May 1903 to Liverpool Corporation. The cranes were useful for small lifting jobs in the days when powered mobile cranes were few and far between.

handbrake and a cab over the crew's heads. In general they were compound engines that had block-style flywheels. For long-distance road running there was, in addition to the normal water tank under the coal bunker, another one known as a belly tank slung under the boiler, giving a total water-carrying capacity of about 325 gallons (1477 litres), sufficient for water stops to be spaced 12 miles (19 km) apart. Road haulage firms like Pickfords of London and Norman Box of Manchester were using road locomotives until the end of the Second World War in 1945. Mac-Larens of Leeds, whose works adjoined those of John Fowler at Hunslet, built some very big road locomotives, one of which, Number 1870 of 1936, was the last steam engine built by them. It is now preserved, after service with a gold mining company, in the museum at Pioneers Park, Johannesburg, South Africa.

PRINCIPAL MECHANICAL FEATURES

THE BOILER

Traction engines burn fuel (mostly coal) and raise steam in what are known as locomotive-type multitubular boilers, developed by George Stephenson of railway fame. Nothing has since proved better, for it is a simple boiler with two principal parts. The straight-sided rear end is the firebox, containing an inner firebox surrounded by water except at the bottom, over which the firegrate is fitted. Secondly, there is the round boiler barrel reaching from the firebox to the smokebox at the front or chimney end of the boiler. A number of tubes conduct the hot fire gases from the firebox to the smokebox, and as they pass through the boiler they generate steam, which accumulates above the water in it. The waste heat and any sparks, after leaving the front end of the boiler tubes, are blown away up the chimney.

As the boiler is under steam pressure, feed water has to be forced into it. For this purpose, each traction engine has either two injectors or one injector and a force-feed pump. An injector is a small gadget made of brass. It has one hole for admitting steam and another for feed water from the engine's water tank. A third orifice to the atmosphere acts as an overflow by which excess steam or water may escape on to the ground. The way to work an injector is first to turn on the water cock. As soon as water begins to run from the overflow pipe, the steam valve should be opened. The inrushing steam will then blow the feed water into the boiler. A few shakes of the handle of the water cock will adjust the water supply precisely and the injector will set to work with a pleasant 'singing' note of its own. More precisely, there is inside the injector a cunning arrangement of variously shaped cones but in simple terms the steam blows the water into the boiler.

Traction engine injectors are designed to work on cold water, and the colder the water the better they function. During hot weather, or if the steam supply valve is not turned off tightly after use, the injector will protest at the warm water by continually 'blowing off'. A remedy is to pour cold water over the body of the injector.

A boiler feed pump has a long steel plunger in it. This plunger is moved slowly up and down the pump barrel and forces water, a squirt at a time, into the boiler. As these pumps are driven off the crankshaft, they are in motion all the time the engine is rotating, but they pump water only when their water cock handle is in the 'on' position.

The average traction engine boiler holds about 100 gallons (450 litres) of water, the level of which has to be maintained some 6 inches (150 mm) above the firebox crownplate, lest the crown becomes red hot and sufficiently pliable for the steam pressure to force it downwards with a violent explosion. There is a safety device in the form of a lead-centred plug which is fitted into the firebox crown. If this plug should become uncovered the lead would melt, allowing steam to rush into the firebox and extinguish the fire. Some drivers, however, did run their engines with a solid brass plug.

ABOVE: *Two Fowler road locomotives hauling a 100 ton transformer from the Hackbridge Electrical Construction Company's works at Hersham in Surrey to Barking Power Station on 14th March 1936. A Scammell motor vehicle, acting as a pusher uphill and brake downhill, is at the rear replacing a Hickey's of Richmond Fowler engine which had overturned during a downhill runaway on an earlier part of the journey. The leading engine, owned by Coulson and Company of Park Royal, London, is B5 Number 9904 of 1904. It is followed by Number 14921 of 1917, owned by E. W. Rudd, haulage contractor of London. Night lights on Coulson's engine are either oil or acetylene on the top side of the smokebox, and electric at the bottom, taking current from a small steam turbo generator. An oil-lit stable lantern, hung beside the right front wheel, shone on the roadside kerb as a steering guide for the engine crew. The nuisance of steam from the safety valve of Number 9904 blowing back into the cab and interfering with vision ahead was avoided by the chute fitted over those valves.*

BELOW: *Fowler B6 road locomotives Numbers 16264 'Jix' and 17105 'Atlas' pull, and Number 16263 'Talisman' pushes, a 90 ton transformer on the last leg of a 170 mile journey from Trafford Park, Manchester, to Ebbw Vale, South Wales, in 1938. Large loads such as this were awkward to move by rail because of limited clearances at some bridges and tunnels. Such jobs, therefore, were subcontracted to firms which specialised in road haulage by steam, in this instance Pickfords. Two crewmen walk alongside, ready to give assistance in case of mishap, when holding chocks were placed behind wheels or other traffic held back. The men's living van is at the rear, for it was their custom to live with the load whilst on the road.*

A spring-loaded safety valve (actually two small valves side by side) is fitted on top of the cylinder casting, where the boiler pressure is always acting upon it. On older forms of safety valve drivers are able, by means of an adjusting screw, to adjust the pressure valves in order to obtain extra pressure to perform a particularly hard piece of work. Some boiler explosions were caused by this malpractice. On most safety valves in use today it is impossible, while the engine is in steam, to adjust the pressure to a higher figure, although by the slackening of a nut it can be decreased.

SINGLE AND COMPOUND ENGINES

An engine with one cylinder is known as a single. Those with two cylinders are called compounds. In the single steam is let into one end of the cylinder and exhausted into the chimney at the end of each stroke. With a compound the steam is made to perform two pushes in order to obtain the maximum amount of effort from it. For example, with a 180 pound pressure engine, during the first piston push in the high-pressure cylinder (which has a smaller diameter) the pressure falls to, say, 100 pounds by the time of exhaust into the low-pressure large cylinder, where a second-stage piston push takes another 80 pounds pressure from the steam before exhaust into the chimney at just above atmospheric pressure. Because a compound uses a greater amount of the pressure in the steam, it is a more economical engine and exhausts more quietly. It was the aim of designers that the power effort of both cylinders of compounds should be equal. Test readings taken under working conditions, however, frequently showed a slightly better output from the high-pressure side. Makers claimed that a compound showed a 25 per cent fuel economy over the single, although 15 to 20 per cent would have been more accurate. Farmers, who provided the coal and water for contractors working on their land, preferred compound plough engines, claiming that they burnt much less coal and consumed one load less of water a day. Whenever extra power was wanted momentarily from a compound, by pushing open the so called 'double high' valve, boiler pressure steam was admitted also into the low-pressure cylinder, with marked effect.

THE VALVE GEAR

Several kinds of valve gear were used on British traction engines, but the Stephenson arrangement, adopted by George Stephenson in the 1840s, was by far the most commonly used. This gear gets all its motion from the revolving crankshaft. Two eccentrics (an eccentric is a form of crank converting circular motion into reciprocating action) are fixed in proper positions on the crankshaft. One of them gives forward and the other backward running. To each eccentric there is attached a rod reaching fowards to a curved link. The foregear rod goes to the top, and the back gear rod to the bottom of the curved link, which has a sliding die block in it. The driver's reversing rod is connected by a lifting arm so that the link may be moved up and down. When the curved link is dropped (by pushing the reversing lever right forward) the foregear eccentric rod is now in line with the valve rod and so the valve rod is now entirely under the control of the foregear eccentric. Steam will be admitted and released from the cylinder in such a way that the motion will turn over in the direction that produces forward working only. Conversely, by pulling the lever right back, the curved link is lifted to bring the back gear eccentric rod in line with the valve rod. In the mid position of the reversing lever, the curved link is lifted halfway only and no motion at all is imparted to the valve rod. This is known as the neutral position, where no steam at all is admitted to the cylinder.

At the front end of the gear is the valve itself, moving backwards and forwards across the cylinder port faces, first admitting the steam into one end of the cylinder and afterwards releasing it to exhaust from the other end. A slide valve, which resembles a shallow lidless metal box made of gun metal, lies face downwards with steam pressure on its outer surfaces holding it tight against the port faces. This is the more usual type of valve used. When the outside edges of

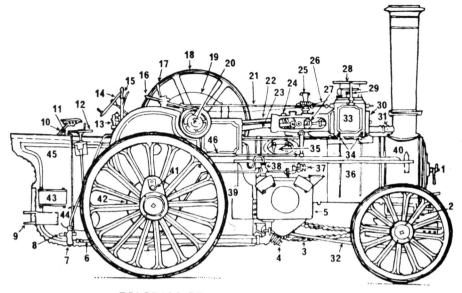

DIAGRAM OF A TRACTION ENGINE
Description of the numbered parts

Part No. — *Description*

1. Smokebox door handles.
2. Perch bracket by which the front axle is secured to the smokebox.
3. Steering chain.
4. Steering gear worm screw.
5. Belly tank carrying extra water.
6. Delivery pipe from injector to the boiler.
7. Injector.
8. Water inlet to injector.
9. Drawbar bracket.
10. Steersman's seat.
11. Injector water handle.
12. Handbrake wheel.
13. Force-feed water pump.
14. Steering wheel.
15. Driver's reversing lever.
16. Gear change lever.
17 Regulator handle.
18. Flywheel.
19. Oil splash plate.
20. End of crankshaft.
21. Regulator rod.
22. Top or foregear eccentric rod.
23. Connecting rod.
24. Curved link of Stephenson valve gear.
25. Governor.
26. Whistle string.
27. Piston crosshead.
28. Safety valves.
29. Whistle.
30. Front cover of single cylinder.
31. Exhaust steam pipe.
32. Stay rod between firebox and front axle.
33. Cylinder.
34. Cylinder waste water cocks.
35. Boiler inspection manhole.
36. Boiler barrel.
37. Injector water delivery clack-box.
38. Water lifter (used with pipe at roadside streams).
39. Firebox outside plate.
40. Smokebox.
41. Main driving pin.
42. Handbrake drum.
43. Water pocket for filling tank by external means.
44. Main water tank.
45. Coal bunker.
46. Reversing rod.

the valve body uncover a cylinder port, steam is admitted and, as soon as an inside edge uncovers a port opening, exhaust steam escapes from the cylinder through the hollow interior of the slide valve directly to the chimney.

Whenever the reversing lever is in the fully forward or backward positions, the valve has maximum travel, which allows a good flow of steam into the cylinder. By 'pulling up' the lever, as drivers say, valve travel is proportionally shortened and less steam is admitted to the cylinder. For hard work, therefore, the lever is kept on either the fore or the back gear stop, while under easier conditions it is 'pulled up' in order to economise on steam.

Many engines made by Marshall, Sons and Company of Gainsborough had the firm's own style of gear, in which a single eccentric, in conjunction with a bell crank and slide box, gives similar valve effects to those obtained from the Stephenson gear.

THE GEARS

Each traction engine has heavy cogwheel gears giving at least two speeds, fast and slow. To change gear the driver has to stop before attempting to slide one gear wheel's teeth into those of another. Some clever drivers boasted how they could change gear without stopping. They could, but it needed fine judgement. The driver of a 12 ton road locomotive hauling 12 tons of furniture to Southampton along the Epsom Road in Guildford around midnight on 9th February 1911 realised that his road train was running away downhill. He attempted to change down from top to bottom gear but missed, with a grinding of gear wheels, and the engine and vans overturned. A hitch-hiker riding on the tail board of the first van was killed.

SPRINGS

It is usual for traction engines to have springs, although rollers and plough engines are entirely unsprung, a feature that makes them rough to ride on a road journey of any length.

BRAKES

In the ordinary meaning of the word, traction engines have no power brakes.

These workmen are riveting new strakes on to a traction engine hind wheel at Tortington Ironworks about 1930. The rivets, heated to a bright cherry red in the blacksmith's shop (off the photograph to left), were taken in long tongs and thrust quickly into the waiting holes. Whilst two men known as 'holders up' held short-handled sledge hammers to buffer up the rivet at the back, the two men at the front hit alternate hammer blows that swelled and locked the rivet tightly in position.

Manstand on Fowler 12 ton compound roller Number 17077 of 1927. Over the steam pressure gauge is the push-button of the 'double-high' valve. Under the long diagonal regulator handle is the battered old tin filled with heavy black oil with an old paintbrush for splashing oil on the open teeth of the gear wheels whilst running on the road. Through the top segment of the large steering wheel can be seen the dim outline of the cylinder block ahead.

Few early engines had even a handbrake, although most now do have them for help descending hills or for parking.

The accepted method for holding back downhill is to shut off steam, open the cylinder waste water cocks and pull up the reversing gear almost to mid gear. By so doing, the piston is made to compress air in the cylinder, imposing upon the engine a work load sufficient to hold it back.

LUBRICATION

In order to withstand the high steam temperatures in the cylinder block, a heavy mineral oil, soluble in water, is needed for the valves and cylinders. Nowadays it is delivered to the block by a mechanical lubricator.

Separate oil cups or plain holes are provided for the other fifty or so points that require oil. For the more important places, such as big ends and eccentrics, plugs made of worsted strands are pushed down the inner pipe of the oil cups, permitting a slow seep of oil downwards to the bearing below. Less important oiling places like axles, piston and valve slides use capillary attraction to lift the oil from the body of the oil cup into its central and open oil pipe. Here, use is made of two or three strands of worsted held in position by a short length of twisted wire. Plug and strand oilers give a simple and reliable method for lubricating traction engines.

FURTHER READING

Bonnett, Harold. *Farming with Steam*. Shire Publications, 1974; reprinted 1984.
Bonnett, Harold. *Saga of the Steam Plough*. Allen and Unwin, 1965.
Bonnett, Harold. *Steam Traction Engines*. Robert Tyndall, 1975.
Clark, Ronald H. *Chronicles of a Country Works*. Percival Marshall, 1952.
Clark, Ronald H. *The English Traction Engine*. Goose and Son, 1960.
Cushing, George, and Starsmore, Ian. *Steam at Thursford*. David and Charles, 1982.
Edmonds, C. *A Little and Often*. Corinthian, 1984.
Haining, Peter. *Traction Engine Companion*. Robert Hale, 1983.
Lane, Michael. *Steam Plough Works*. Northgate Publishing Company, 1980.
Tew, David. *Traction Engines and the Law*. National Traction Engine Club, 1981.
Whitehead, R. H. *Wallis and Steevens — A History*. Road Locomotive Society, 1983.

PLACES TO VISIT

Bicton Park Countryside Collection, East Budleigh, Budleigh Salterton, Devon EX9 7DP. Telephone: Colaton Raleigh (0395) 68465.

Breamore Countryside Museum, Breamore House, Breamore, Fordingbridge, Hampshire. Telephone: Downton (0725) 22270.

Bressingham Live Steam Museum, Bressingham, Diss, Norfolk IP22 2AB. Telephone: Bressingham (037 988) 386.

Country Life Museum, Sandy Bay, Exmouth, Devon EX8 5PT. Telephone: Exmouth (0395) 274533.

Easton Farm Park, Easton, Woodbridge, Suffolk. Telephone: Wickham Market (0728) 746475.

Hollycombe Steam Collection, Hollycombe House, Liphook, Hampshire. Telephone: Liphook (0428) 723233.

Hunday National Tractor and Farm Museum, Newton, Stocksfield, Northumberland. Telephone: Stocksfield (0661) 842553.

Kew Bridge Engines Trust (Living Steam Museum), Green Dragon Lane, Brentford, Middlesex TW8 0EF. Telephone: 01-568 4757.

Leicestershire Museum of Technology, Abbey Pumping Station, Corporation Road, Abbey Lane, Leicester. Telephone: Leicester (0533) 661330.

Levens Hall Steam Collection, Levens Hall, Kendal, Cumbria. Telephone: Sedgwick (053 95) 60321.

The Long Shop, Main Street, Leiston, Suffolk. Telephone: Leiston (0728) 830550.

Museum of East Anglian Life, Abbotts Hall, Stowmarket, Suffolk IP14 1DL. Telephone: Stowmarket (0449) 612229.

Museum of Lincolnshire Life, The Old Barracks, Burton Road, Lincoln LN1 3LY. Telephone: Lincoln (0522) 28448.

National Motor Museum, John Montagu Building, Beaulieu, Brockenhurst, Hampshire SO4 7ZN. Telephone: Beaulieu (0590) 612345.

North of England Open Air Museum, Beamish, Stanley, County Durham DH9 0RG. Telephone: Stanley (0207) 231811.

Nottingham Industrial Museum, Courtyard Buildings, Wollaton Park, Nottingham NG8 2AE. Telephone: Nottingham (0602) 284602.

Strumpshaw Hall Steam Museum, Strumpshaw, Norwich, Norfolk. Telephone: Norwich (0603) 712339.

Thursford Collection, Thursford, Fakenham, Norfolk. Telephone: Fakenham (0328) 3839.

ACKNOWLEDGEMENTS

Photographs on the following pages are acknowledged to: Dick Carter (Send and Ripley History Society), page 3; *Eastern Daily Press*, page 22 (upper); High Wycombe Public Library, page 24 (upper); Herr Hubler, page 12 (upper); Kodak Ltd, page 6 (upper); Cadbury Lamb, cover; C. G. Mileham, pages 24 (lower), 25, 27; Museum of East Anglian Life, page 9; Museum of English Rural Life, page 1; A. T. Oliver, page 19; William Oswald, pages 14, 15; James Penfold Ltd, pages 5 (lower), 8 (upper), 17, 18, 20 (upper), 30; W. P. Ridley, page 12 (lower); John Russell, page 11 (lower); Science Museum, page 2; Sidney Shaw, page 8 (lower); Société Francais, page 21 (upper); Derek Stoyel, page 10. All other photographs are from the author's collection.